GCSE
Questions and Answers

BIOLOGY

KEY STAGE 4

Jackie Callaghan & Morton Jenkins

Chief Examiners

Letts
EDUCATIONAL

SERIES EDITOR: BOB McDUELL

Contents

Reflex	Stimulus	Response
Coughing	Irritant in the throat	Contraction of abdominal muscles and expiratory intercostal muscles; relaxation of the diaphragm
Swallowing	Food at the back of the throat	Soft palate is raised; epiglottis is closed; peristalsis takes place
Blinking	Object coming towards the eye	Contraction of eyelid muscles
Knee-jerk	Pressure/pain on knee	Contraction of flexor muscles
Pupil contraction/dilation	Change in light intensity	Contraction of muscles of the iris

Drugs and the nervous system

Tobacco is not addictive in the sense that narcotic drugs are. However, it does pose serious health problems, as it tends to shorten life and seems to contribute to many diseases.

Alcohol is a depressant. Used excessively, it leads to alcoholism. Alcohol can cause organic diseases which may be fatal. It can be antisocial and is dangerous when used by people who drive.

Misuse of **drugs** can be harmful to users and may even cause death. Drug addiction can be a psychological problem, a physical one, or both. *Narcotic drugs* can become physically addictive. People who take them habitually often do so in order to escape from problems. This is psychological addiction. But as the body builds up a drug tolerance, so addicts must take more and more in order to 'escape'. Physically, the body demands more in order to avoid painful *withdrawal symptoms*. Narcotics are illegal, with just a few available on prescription. Consequently, many addicts spend much of their time looking for ways to obtain drugs and invariably turn to crime, which creates problems for both them and society in general.

Chemical control

Ductless glands are called **endocrine glands**. They secrete *hormones* directly into the blood stream.

Glands are controlled by their influence on each other, by feedback, and by the nervous system. Their delicate balance is maintained by *homeostatic mechanisms*. If any one of the endocrine glands slows down or becomes overactive, the chemical balance is upset and the body reacts, making the person feel ill.

Nutrition

Our bodies need a variety of complex organic nutrients. They also need minerals, water and fibre. There are three kinds of organic nutrients that are needed in bulk: carbohydrates, fats and proteins.

The digestive system is a tube divided into various regions. This tube is called the alimentary canal. Each region is a specialized organ. Each organ is adapted for performing certain phases of the digestive process. Both our teeth and muscles in the alimentary canal break down the food we eat, mechanically. Many glands pour enzymes into the digestive tract. These enzymes break food down chemically. These mechanical and chemical changes must take place before food can be absorbed and used by our body cells.

If you need to revise this subject more thoroughly, see the relevant topics in the *Letts* **GCSE** *Biology Study Guide or CD-ROM*.

1 (a) The diagram below shows part of the human digestive system.

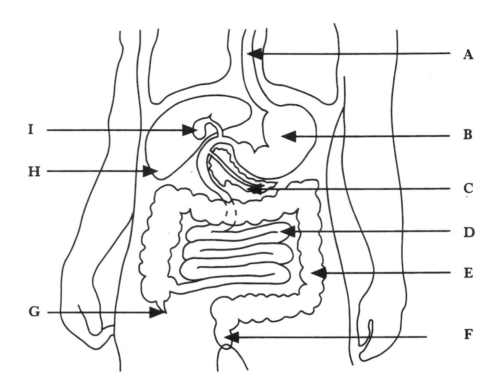

(i) Complete the table by inserting letters from the diagram to identify the named parts of the digestive system.

Part of digestive system	Letter
Liver	
Pancreas	
Oesophagus	
Appendix	

(4)

(ii) Describe **one** function of the part labelled **E**.

.... (1)

(iii) Describe two features of the small intestine which help in the absorption of the products of digestion.

1. ....

2. .... (2)

(b) The table below gives the percentages of different types of tissue found in the body of a typical male adult.

Body tissues	Mass (%)
Muscle	45
Bone	15
Fat (essential)	3
Fat (storage)	12
Other tissues	25

Part of this information is presented in Pie Chart 1 below.
Pie Chart 2 shows the percentage for a typical female adult.

Pie Chart 1
Typical Male Adult

Pie Chart 2
Typical Female Adult

(i) Complete Pie Chart 1, using the information from the table. (2)

(ii) Which tissue has the greatest percentage mass in both males and females?

.... (1)

(iii) Which adult contains more fat in total?

.... (1)

(iv) A man weighs 80 kilograms. Calculate the expected mass of the muscle tissue in his body.

.... kg (1)

SQA 1995

2 (a) A group of pupils carried out an experiment to illustrate digestion in mammals.

1. The pupils mixed $20cm^3$ of starch suspension with $5cm^3$ of 'digestive juice' in a beaker.
2. They immediately tested a sample of the mixture for the presence of starch and for maltose.
3. They took a second sample after 15 minutes and again carried out the tests for starch and maltose.

Time	Starch	Maltose
At start	present	absent
After 15 minutes	absent	present

(i) Name the enzyme present in the digestive juice.

.... (1)

(ii) Name a part of the digestive system in a mammal where this enzyme is produced.

.... (1)

(b) The list below contains statements about enzyme activity.

List
1. Substrate of an enzyme
2. Optimum conditions for an enzyme
3. Enzyme action is specific
4. Increased rate of chemical reaction
5. Products of enzyme action

(i) Using pH as your example, explain the meaning of **statement 2**.

....

.... (1)

(ii) Select all the statements from the list above which relate to **each** of the following sentences.

A statement can be used **once**, **more than once** or **not at all**.

	Statement Numbers
The enzyme pepsin acts only on protein molecules.	
Protein molecules are broken down to form short chains of amino acids.	

(2)

SQA 1995

3 The diagram below represents part of the structure of the hip joint.

(a) Complete each of the boxes with the name or function of the part of the joint indicated.

Name	Function
	Holds the bones of a joint together

Name	Function
Cartilage	

Name	Function
Synovial fluid	

(2)

(b) Explain why two muscles are needed to control the movements of the bones of a hinge joint.

....

....

....

.... (2)

SQA 1995

4 The diagram shows a section through the leaf of a green plant.

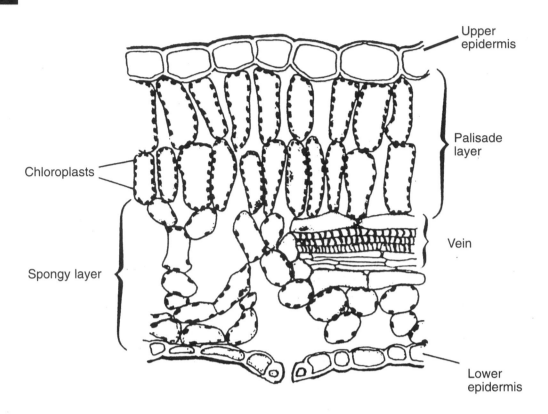

(a) (i) Which layer of this leaf contains most chloroplasts?

.... (1)

(ii) Which layer of this leaf will receive most sunlight?

.... (1)

(b) How do the air spaces in the leaf help it to photosynthesise well?

....

....

.... (3)

SEG 1995

5 Insulin-secreting cells can be injected into a person's abdomen. The cells are in jelly capsules and a single treatment could replace daily injections of insulin for several months. The jelly capsule allows insulin molecules to pass through but keeps out antibodies and white blood cells.

(a) Where, in the body, is insulin normally produced?

.... (1)

(b) Name the condition which is treated by the method described above.

.... (1)

(c) State why this condition cannot be **cured** by injecting insulin.

.... (1)

(d) What would be the effect of (i) antibodies and (ii) white blood cells if they were able to pass through the jelly to the cells?

    (i)   Antibodies (1)

    (ii)   White blood cells (1)

(e) Explain why glucagon has the opposite effect to insulin.

....

....

....

.... (3)

(f) The production of insulin by biotechnology involves the following steps. They are in the wrong order. Use the letters A-E to show below the correct order.

   A   Separating and purifying insulin.
   B   Putting the gene into the genetic material of bacteria.
   C   Identifying the human gene controlling the production of insulin.
   D   Isolating the gene which controls the production of insulin.
   E   Growing large numbers of genetically altered bacteria.

.... (5)

(g) State one advantage of using insulin made by biotechnology.

.... (1)

WJEC 1996

QUESTIONS

6 The gemsbok is a large herbivore that lives in herds in desert areas of South Africa. Gemsboks feed on plants that are adapted to living in dry conditions. There are not many rivers, lakes or ponds that can provide drinking water for the animals. The desert areas are hot during the day but cool at night. As the air cools at night it becomes moist, and the plants absorb the moisture.

(a) A few lions live in the desert areas. They hunt and feed on the gemsboks.
Use information from the drawing of the gemsbok to suggest **two** ways in which it could avoid being killed by lions.

1 ....

2 .... (2)

(b) The graphs show the water content of the desert grass and the times of day that the gemsboks feed.

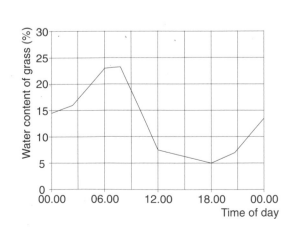

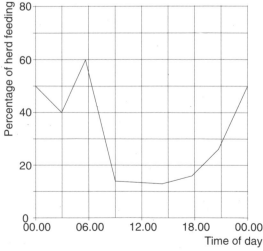

(i) Describe how the water content of the grass changes during the day.

.... (1)

(ii) Suggest why the water content of the grass changes.

.... (1)

(c) (i) Between which times of day are more than 25% of the herd feeding?

.... (1)

(ii) Suggest an advantage to the gemsbok of feeding mainly at these times.

....

.... (2)

(d) Although the gemsbok lives in hot conditions, it does not sweat. During the day its body temperature can rise, but it is important that blood reaching the brain does not rise above 40°C. The drawing shows how the blood system is adapted to cool the blood which flows to the brain.

vein
(blood at 37°C)   brain

blood vessels
in wall of
nasal cavity

artery to brain
(blood at 40°C)

rete (veins and
arteries split into
small vessels)

nostril

vein to
heart

artery (blood at 43°C)

(i) Suggest an advantage to the gemsbok of **not** sweating.

.... (1)

(ii) Explain how the blood is cooled in the cavities of the nose.

....

.... (2)

(iii) How does the structure of the rete help in keeping the brain cool?

....

.... (2)

**REVISION
SUMMARY**

Cell growth and reproduction

Organisms grow by **mitosis**.

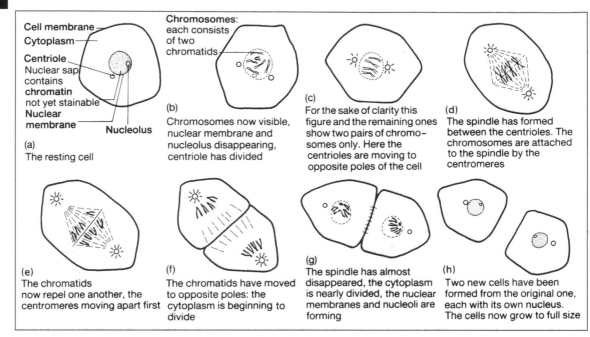

Stages in mitosis

Each daughter cell produced in mitosis has the *diploid chromosome number*. Further, the chromosomes of the daughter cells are identical to those of the mother cell. All body cells in all members of the same species contain the same kind and number of chromosomes.

Sperms and eggs are produced by a different kind of division, known as **meiosis**.

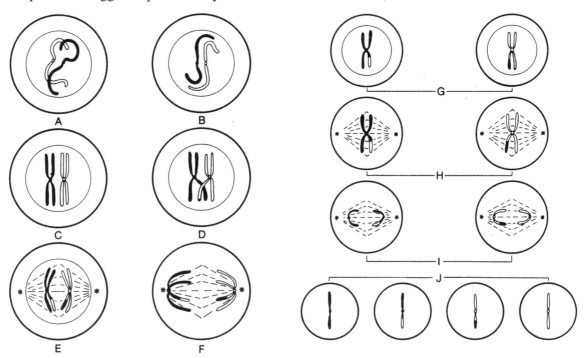

Key: Maternal chromosome is white
Paternal chromosome is black; Diploid number = 2

Meiosis in a gamete-forming cell

The stages in meiosis, as shown in the previous diagram, are as follows:

❶ Each *chromosome* moves towards, and begins to pair with, its partner. The pairing process results in a very *close contact* along the whole of the length of the chromosomes (B). Thus the first stage of *meiosis* differs from that in mitosis. At the start of mitosis the chromosomes consist of two chromatids which are formed by duplication, but in meiosis whole *pairs* of chromosomes come together.

❷ While in this close union, the chromosomes shorten and thicken, and each becomes *duplicated* into **two chromatids** (C). At this stage the *nuclear membrane* begins to disintegrate.

❸ Along the length of the pairs of chromosomes, individual **chromatids cross** one another in complex ways. As a result of this, chromatids **exchange** various sections (D). The force of attraction that up to this point has held the pairs of chromosomes together now ceases to operate fully, and the pairs of chromosomes begin to *separate* (E). (In the diagram for simplicity only one cross-over is shown.)

❹ The chromosomes separate completely and move to *opposite* poles of the cell (F). The *cytoplasm divides* (G). At this point, each daughter cell still has the *diploid* number of chromosomes, but because of *crossing over* of sections of the chromatids, **genes** from one partner have been mixed with genes from the other partner.

❺ Each new cell undergoes a *mitotic* division. The chromosomes, each consisting of *two complete chromatids* (even though parts have been exchanged), line up along the centre of the new cell (H). One set of chromatids passes to each pole of the cell. Each new set of chromosomes starts to form a nucleus (I).

❻ A division of the cytoplasm occurs and nuclear membranes reappear. As a result, **four gametes**, each with the *haploid* number of chromosomes, have been formed from an original *diploid* cell (J).

The *significance* of meiosis is:

(a) The formation of cells with **half** the diploid number of chromosomes.

(b) **Mixing of genes** between pairs of chromosomes contributing to **variation** within the chromosomes.

Meiosis involves two stages of division. The cells that result contain the *haploid chromosome number*. When these cells join in fertilization, the diploid number is restored.

Principles of heredity

It was the work of Gregor Mendel (1822–1884) with garden peas that opened up the field of **heredity** to science. Mendel's hypotheses about **genes**, which he called factors, have become basic principles of **genetics**. Among these principles are the ideas that genes:

- control heredity,
- occur in pairs, and
- may be *dominant* or *recessive*.

The genetic material

Many years have passed since Gregor Mendel's experiments with garden peas opened up the science of genetics. Since 1900, scientists have probed deeper and deeper into the mysteries of the living cell and its genetic material. Most of the traits we inherit are necessary and helpful. Some are harmful. We are finding out more and more about these genetic problems. Often, learning the cause of a problem leads to its correction. We are beginning to learn the effects of genes in causing such disorders as cystic fibrosis, Huntington's chorea, haemophilia and many other conditions.

Genes sometimes *mutate* and a major cause of mutations is high energy radiation. Radiation from artifical sources and natural sources will cause changes in the structure of genes, leading to mutation.

In the body cells of mammals, one of the pairs of chromosomes carries the genes which determine gender. These are called sex chromosomes. In females, the sex chromosomes are the same (XX); in males the sex chromosomes are different (XY). The X chromosome can carry more genes than the Y chromosome and some of these genes do not have a corresponding partner on the Y chromosome in males. Such genes are said to be sex-linked. If these genes are harmful in their recessive form, they can cause males to suffer certain disorders, allowing females to carry the allele where it is masked by its dominant form. If the female has the dominant 'normal' allele, then she will not suffer from the disorder.

Many disorders are inherited in humans by being caused by genes having been passed from parents to children.

Cystic fibrosis (abnormal bronchiole and pancreas function) can be passed on by parents, neither of whom has the disease, because it is caused by a recessive allele. Each parent could have the dominant allele masking the recessive.

N = normal (dominant); n = cystic fibrosis (recessive)

Parents	Nn		x		Nn	
Children	NN	Nn		Nn		nn

The child with the nn genotype would suffer from cystic fibrosis, i.e. a 25% chance.

Huntington's chorea (muscle spasms and speech impairment) is passed on by one parent who has the disease because it is caused by a dominant allele.

H = Huntington's chorea (dominant); h = normal (recessive)

Parents	Hh		x		hh	
Children	Hh	Hh		hh		hh

The children with the Hh genotype would suffer from Huntington's chorea, i.e. a 50% chance.

Haemophilia (inability of the blood to clot) is passed on to sons by females who do not suffer from the disorder.

XX = female; XY = male

H = normal blood clotting (dominant); h = haemophilia (recessive)

Parents	X^HX^h		x		X^HY	
Children	X^HX^H	X^HY		X^hX^H		X^hY

The children with the X^hY genotype would suffer from haemophilia, i.e. 25% chance or a 50% chance in sons.

Applied genetics

For many centuries, people have worked at breeding improved strains of plants and animals. Three important methods of breeding are **mass selection**, **hybridization**, and **inbreeding**. Mass selection involves choosing the parents for further breeding from a large number of individuals. Hybridization is the crossing of two different strains. An example of inbreeding is self pollination in plants. Over several generations, the offspring with the desired traits are sorted out by mass selection. In the end, a pure strain is produced.

Another form of applied genetics is **genetic engineering**. This relies on isolating a useful gene from one organism and putting it into another of a different species. For example, scientists often isolate genes from human chromosomes which control the production of certain hormones. They put these useful genes into bacteria or yeast cells. The human genes are transferred to the bacteria or yeast to increase production of the hormone. The microbes multiply very rapidly and can be cultured relatively cheaply. In fact, they can provide almost unlimited amounts of substances that are practically unobtainable in bulk in any other way.

1   The information below is about insulin.

- Insulin is a *hormone*, produced by the pancreas, which reduces the concentration of glucose in the blood.

- People who cannot produce insulin, or not enough of it, are called diabetics.

- Diabetics usually need daily injections of insulin.

- For many years this insulin has been extracted from the pancreas of pigs, sheep and cattle.

- Scientists can now produce human insulin using a technique known as genetic-engineering.

(a) What are *hormones*?

    ....

    ....

    ....(2)

(b) The diagram below shows some of the stages involved in the production of genetically-engineered human insulin.

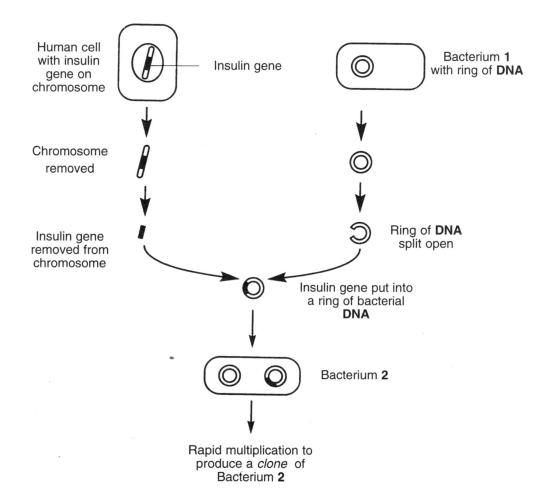

Human cell with insulin gene on chromosome — Insulin gene

Bacterium **1** with ring of **DNA**

Chromosome removed

Insulin gene removed from chromosome

Ring of **DNA** split open

Insulin gene put into a ring of bacterial **DNA**

Bacterium **2**

Rapid multiplication to produce a *clone* of Bacterium **2**

QUESTIONS

(i) How is the insulin gene removed from the human chromosome?

.... (1)

(ii) The *clone* of bacterium **2** produces large quantities of insulin.

    (A) What is a *clone*?

    ....

    .... (2)

    (B) Explain why bacteria are suitable organisms to use for this purpose.

    ....

    ....

    ....

    .... (3)

(c) Explain **one** advantage genetically-engineered insulin has compared with that extracted from animals.

    ....

    .... (2)

SEG 1995

2 A type of snail occurs on an island in the Pacific Ocean. The snails are black with yellow stripes or completely black. When the striped type is crossed (bred) with the black type, all the young are striped.
When two black types are crossed, all the young are black.

(a) Complete the key:

    Dominant allele ....   Recessive allele .... (1)

(b) Sometimes a cross between a striped snail and a black snail produced 50% striped young and 50% black young.
Use the box below to explain the mating between the striped snail and the black snail.

Genotypes: Striped ....Black .... (1)

(1)

(c) Use the box below to explain the mating between two heterozygous striped snails.

(2)

(d) Until 1950 the island was covered in grass. The snails were eaten by birds and there were many more striped snails than black. In 1950, nuclear bomb testing began on the island. This resulted in the loss of grass and blackening of rocks. Radioactivity prevented scientists visiting the island for many years.
Eventually, scientists visited the island. They found many birds but very little grass. There were more black snails than striped ones, and a new brown type of snail was found.
Using the information and your knowledge, explain:

(i) the change in numbers of black snails;

....

....

.... (3)

(ii) the sudden appearance of the brown variety.

....

.... (2)

WJEC 1998

3 The diagram below shows the inheritance of eye colour in a family. The gene for brown eyes is dominant (**B**) and the gene for blue eyes is recessive (**b**).

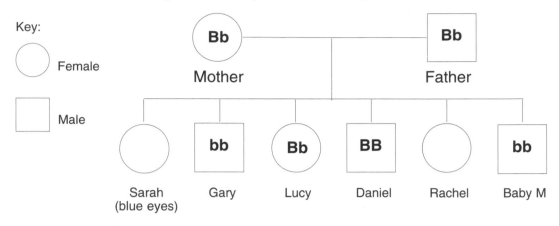

Key:

◯ Female

▢ Male

Mother **Bb** —— **Bb** Father

Sarah (blue eyes) | Gary **bb** | Lucy **Bb** | Daniel **BB** | Rachel | Baby M **bb**

(a) Which of the following statements is true?

A Lucy and Daniel both have blue eyes

B Lucy and Daniel have different coloured eyes

C Lucy and Daniel have the same coloured eyes

D All the males in the family have brown eyes

Answer: statement.................is true (1)

(b) What is the sex and eye colour of baby M?

.... (2)

(c) (i) Daniel's **genotype** is **BB**. What is Sarah's **genotype**?

.... (1)

(ii) Explain how you worked out your answer.

.... (1)

In this family, Rachel has an identical twin. Rachel has brown eyes.

(d) (i) Who is Rachel's identical twin?

.... (1)

(ii) Explain how you decided on your answer.

.... (2)

Edexcel 1995

4 Busy Lizzies are small plants which are easily grown and produce large numbers of white, pink or red flowers all through the summer.

(a) In Busy Lizzies the allele for red flowers (**R**) is dominant to the allele for white flowers (**r**).

A red-flowered Busy Lizzie (**RR**) was cross-pollinated with a white-flowered Busy Lizzie (**rr**). The seeds produced by this cross were grown to produce an **F1** generation of plants all with red flowers.

(i) What is meant by cross-pollination?

....

....

.... (2)

(ii) Why did all the **F1** generation of plants have red flowers?

....

....

.... (2)

(iii) Two of these **F1** red-flowered plants were cross-pollinated. The resulting seeds were grown to produce an **F2** generation of plants.

Use a genetic diagram to explain the genotypes and phenotypes of the **F2** plants.

You will be awarded up to **two** marks for the clarity of your genetic diagram.

....

....

....

....

....

.... (6)

25

QUESTIONS

(b) Imagine that on a remote, uninhabited island scientists discovered colonies of Busy Lizzies growing and that most of these plants produced blue flowers.

These plants could have evolved as a result of *natural selection* in action on a *mutant* **blue**-flowering Busy Lizzie plant.

(i) Explain how a *mutant* (genetic mutation) can arise by referring to the way DNA replicates.

....

....

....

.... (3)

(ii) Explain how *natural selection* could have produced these colonies of **blue**-flowering Busy Lizzie plants

....

....

....

....

....

....

....

.... (3)

SEG 1995

Many people used to take **natural resources** for granted. We have wasted many of these resources and caused thousands of hectares of land to become useless.

- An increase in population has caused mass property development and a need to increase crop yields.

- The increased use of fertilizers, pesticides, silage, etc. has had an adverse effect on the environment, often because the chemicals involved in these treatments find their way into water.

- Over-use of land has caused *soil erosion*.

- An increase in industry and transport has increased *air pollution*: e.g. emissions of sulphur dioxide and oxides of nitrogen cause acid rain; carbon dioxide increases the *Greenhouse Effect* and CFCs damage the ozone layer.

  Large numbers of people, as well as industry, cause pollution problems. Pollution can be defined as anything which, when added to the environment, destroys its purity.

- **Biodegradable substances** are broken down by *bacteria*. This releases minerals for *recycling*. However, there is a limit as to how much can be taken care of in this way.

- Non-biodegradable substances are not broken down. In fact, they may be toxic to organisms in the environment.

- Air can be polluted by many chemicals, some of which are poisonous to plants and animals.

- Radioactive particles can cause tissue damage and death. It is most important that people realise the effects of human action and do something about them.

The population of the world as a whole has been *growing steadily*, though in individual countries there have been *fluctuations* in population size as people have migrated to newly discovered territories or have gone off in search of new food and mineral sources. Malthus, in 1798, suggested that because the population *increases faster* than food production there should be some sort of **birth control**. The growth of the world's population is now much faster than it has been in the past for the following reasons:

❶ The **increased effectiveness of medical science in saving lives** and virtually wiping out many formerly fatal diseases, such as *diphtheria* and *smallpox*.

❷ Practically all mothers and babies survive childbirth because of **improved pre- and post-natal medical care**.

❸ Increased lifespan in the Western industrial countries due to a **better diet** than that enjoyed by our ancestors.

❹ **Agricultural development**.

❺ **Industrial development** due to technological advances leading to greater potential for trade and greater affluence.

Two consequences of an increasing population growth rate are:

- **shortage of food**,

- **pollution**.

If you need to revise this subject more thoroughly, see the relevant topics in the *Letts* **GCSE Biology Study Guide or CD-ROM.**

1 The diagram below shows the proportions of males and females of different ages in the human population in two countries: Honduras and Sweden.

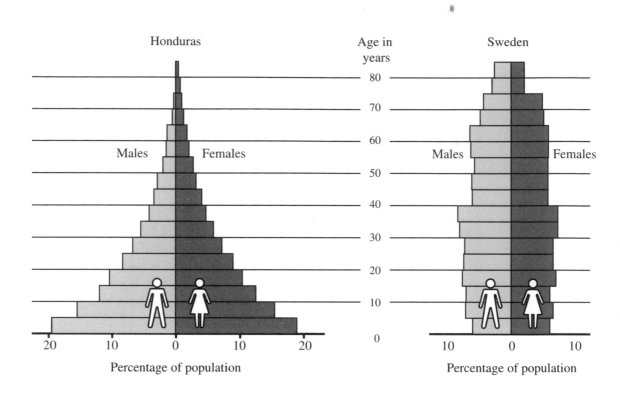

(a) Honduras is a developing country in tropical Central America. Sweden is a developed country in Western Europe. In both Honduras and Sweden, most children are born to parents aged between 20 and 40 years. Give evidence from the diagram which shows that, in proportion to the whole population, Honduras has

(i) a higher birth rate than Sweden; ....

.... (1)

(ii) a higher death rate than Sweden for children in the first ten years of life.

....

.... (2)

(b) Suggest and explain **two** factors which might cause Honduras to have a higher death rate for children in the first 10 years of life.

1 ....

....

.... (2)

2 ....

....

.... (2)

SEG 1997

2 Carbon Dioxide (CO_2) gas is found in the atmosphere.

(a) (i) Name a process which removes CO_2 from the atmosphere.

.... (1)

The burning of fossil fuels releases CO_2 into the atmosphere.

(ii) State one other way in which CO_2 is released into the atmosphere.

.... (1)

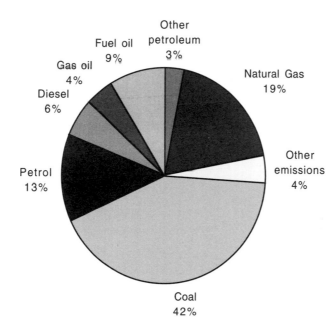

Figure 1 Carbon dioxide emissions
by type of fuel, 1990 UK

(iii) Study Figure 1. What was the source of the **largest proportion** of the carbon dioxide
emitted by machinery using fuel in 1990?

.... (1)

29

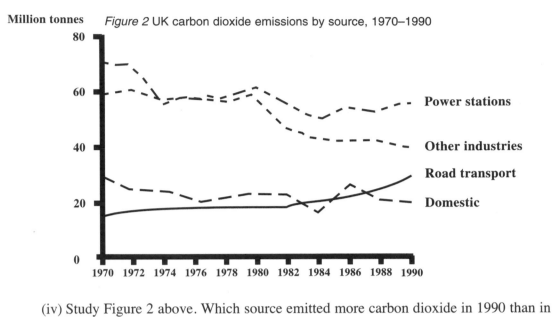

Million tonnes

Figure 2 UK carbon dioxide emissions by source, 1970–1990

(iv) Study Figure 2 above. Which source emitted more carbon dioxide in 1990 than in 1980?

.... (1)

(b) (i) Name the process in which CO_2 contributes to global warming.

.... (1)

(ii) Explain how this process leads to a rise in global warming.

....

....

....

....

....

....

....

.... (4)

NEAB 1996

3 Lichens are plant-like organisms which are found growing on buildings and tree bark. Lichens are easily damaged by sulphur dioxide gas in the air. Table 1 shows the number of lichen species found at different distances from the centre of an industrial city.

Distance from city centre in km	Number of lichen species
0	1
2	4
4	8
6	14
8	20
10	12
12	20
14	29

(a) (i) Plot a line graph of the data in the table on the graph paper below.   (3)

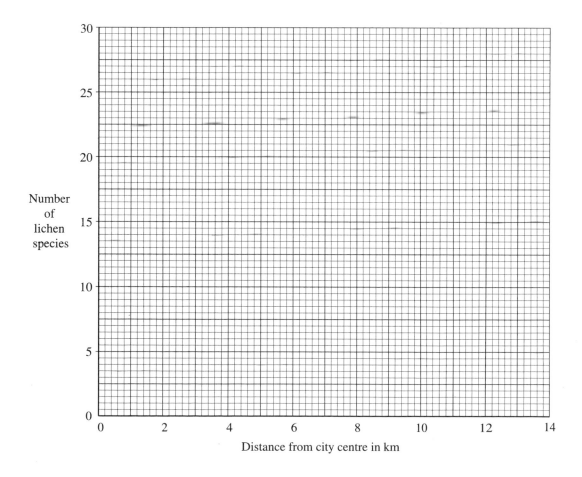

Number of lichen species

Distance from city centre in km

(ii) What happens to the number of species of lichens with an increase in distance from the city centre of 0 to 8 km?

.... (1)

(iii) The city was surrounded by a motorway. From the graph, suggest the approximate distance of the motorway from the city centre. Give reasons for your answer.

Distance ....km

Reasons ....

....

....

.... (3)

(b) **Table 2** gives the names of five lichens and the highest amount of sulphur dioxide in the air in which each can survive.

Name of lichen	Highest amount of sulphur dioxide in which lichens can survive in μg per m^3
Lobaria	30
Evernia	35
Parmelia	60
Xanthoria	70
Lecanora	150

Table 2

(i) Only one species of lichen was found growing at the city centre. From the table, which species is this most likely to be?

.... (1)

(ii) The level of sulphur dioxide near the motorway was 50 μg per m^3. Give the names of those lichens you would expect to find growing near the motorway.

.... (1)

(c) Describe **one** harmful effect of sulphur dioxide on human health.

.... (1)

SEG 1997

4 Read the following passage carefully.

Adapted from *Algal Blooms in Scottish Lochs* from Data Support, WWF Scotland/Scottish Natural Heritage.

Loch Leven is a very important National Nature Reserve. It has the biggest concentration of breeding ducks in Britain and up to 40 000 waterbirds of various kinds visit it each winter.

The loch is naturally rich in nutrients such as phosphate and nitrates, but the levels have been increased because of human activity in the surrounding area. One result has been the appearance of massive blue-green algal blooms in summer. These are composed of microscopic plants which multiply rapidly and turn the water a deep green colour. These microscopic plants release poisonous chemicals when they die and decompose.

The key nutrient in producing an algal bloom is phosphate. Phosphates enter the loch in discharges from a local woollen mill, in domestic sewage and in run-off from the surrounding farmland.

Following a particularly intense algal bloom in 1992, the woollen mill further reduced the phosphates in its discharges and the sewage works installed equipment to remove phosphates from the water it discharged into the loch. Controls have also been imposed on housing development in the area to ensure that phosphate from domestic sewage remains at low levels.

Answer the questions.

(a) Why is Loch Leven Nature Reserve an important site?

.... (1)

(b) What caused the outbreaks of algal blooms in the loch?

.... (1)

(c) Why were efforts made to prevent the formation of algal blooms?

.... (1)

(d) Name **two** sources of the phosphate pollution in Loch Leven.

1 ....

2 .... (2)

(e) Describe **one** way in which phosphate from domestic sewage is being controlled.

.... (1)

(f) The bar chart below shows the mass of phosphate entering the loch each day from different sources in three particular years.

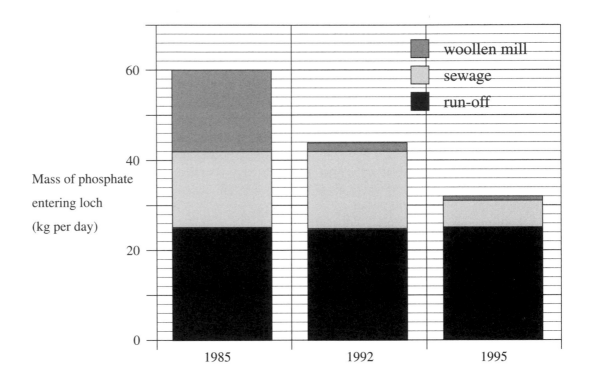

(i) Which major source of phosphate pollution remained the same over the period for which information is given?

.... (1)

(ii) What mass of phosphate entered the loch each day in discharges from the woollen mill in 1985?

.... kg/day (1)

SQA 1997

5 In 1992 elephants living on the shores of Lake Kariba in Zimbabwe were slowly starving because they lost the use of their muscular trunks to obtain food. They had a problem with floppy trunks. All the affected elephants lived in the area of Zimbabwe subjected to severe drought. The drought caused the lake to become smaller. Lake Kariba is used for fishing, tourism and water sports but not for human water supplies. Lead fishing weights, petrol, exhaust fumes, discarded batteries and oil filters from boats are all sources of lead pollution. Lead is a poisonous metal which affects the nervous system.

Use the information above and your knowledge of pollution to answer the following:

(a) State the link between drought and the effects of lead pollution on the elephants.

....

.... (1)

(b) Suggest why the elephants' trunks were floppy.

....

....

.... (2)

(c) Describe how lead pollution in the lake might affect humans.

....

....

.... (2)

(d) The graph shows changes in the size of a protected population of elephants in Zimbabwe, over a period of eleven years.

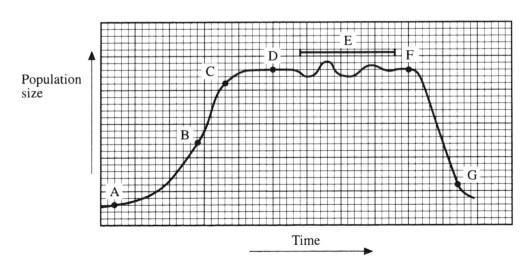

Complete the table by writing a letter from the graph which correctly identifies **each** factor affecting population size.

Factors affecting population size	Letter
Birth rate and death rate are equal	
Short-term environmental change (drought)	
Population growing without limits	
Effects of lead pollution being seen	

(4)

WJEC 1996

All organisms depend on their surroundings to stay alive.

There is a thin layer of life starting a few feet below the ground and extending through the lower atmosphere of our planet. It is called the *biosphere*. It may be considered as one huge *ecosystem*. Or, it may be divided into many small ecosystems. An *ecosystem* is an environment in which living and non-living things affect one another. It is also a system in which materials are recycled. Living organisms are the community. Groups of the same kind of organisms are called populations.

The non-living part of the ecosystem is called the *physical environment* or *habitat*. It has much influence on the biotic community.

A stable population density is important to a balanced ecosystem. Many factors can change population density. Lack of food, for example, will cause a population to decrease. Removal of natural enemies will usually make it temporarily increase. These same factors influence human population density.

Physical factors of an environment (abiotic factors)

❶ Light intensity is particularly important because of its function in photosynthesis.

❷ Oxygen and carbon dioxide are important because of their functions in respiration and photosynthesis, respectively.

❸ Temperature is important because of the influence it has on the rate of chemical reactions going on in all living things.

❹ A balanced supply of minerals is essential to all living things as part of their nutrition.

❺ Water is essential because it makes up a large proportion of protoplasm and all chemical reactions in living things take place in solution.

Biotic factors

All living organisms have some influence upon the outside environment of their neighbours. This influence may be small, such as in a limited competition for water or light. On the other hand it may be very great. For example, many animals play an important part in the outside environment of plants. Some animals pollinate flowers; others disperse seeds; some are the carriers of plant disease; some trample vegetation. Among animals, humans have had the greatest impact on the environment of other organisms.

The total outside environment, consisting of both abiotic and biotic factors, determines which species come together to form a natural community in any one place.

Life in communities

Three sorts of relationships are recognized:

❶ **Competition**: may be between the many members of a given species, or between members of different species.

❷ **Dependence**: all animals are dependent on plants for a supply of food and oxygen.

❸ **Interdependence**: while some organisms compete with one another, and some are totally dependent upon others, there are some ways in which all the species in a community are interdependent.

> If you need to revise this subject more thoroughly, see the relevant topics in the *Letts* GCSE *Biology Study Guide or CD-ROM.*

1 The drawing shows a
freshwater aquarium
in a laboratory.

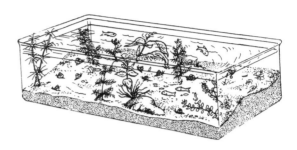

(a) The diagram shows a food web for some of the organisms which live in this aquarium.

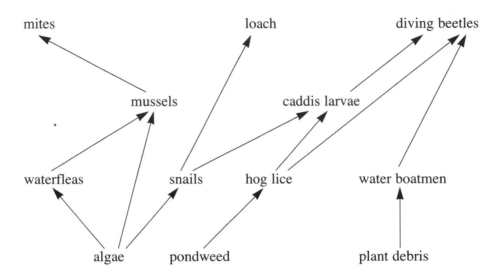

Use the information from the food web to construct a food chain which contains four
organisms.

....

.... (2)

(b) (i) Give four factors which might affect the size of the population of algae in the
aquarium.

1. ....

2. ....

3. ....

4. .... (4)

(ii) Explain how an increase in the population of algae might affect the population of

1. the water fleas:

....

....

2. the mussels:

....

.... (4)

(c) There are two loach in the aquarium. These are fish about 5 cm in length which feed on snails. There are 30 snails in the aquarium. These are 5 mm in diameter and they feed only on algae. Algae are single-celled plants about 1/100 mm in diameter.

Construct and label a pyramid of numbers for the above organisms.

(2)

(d) The organisms which live in the aquarium make up a community. They use the materials in the aquarium, but the amounts of materials do not change very much.

Explain as fully as you can how this balance is maintained.

....

....

.... (2)

NEAB 1995

2 (a) Name the energy source on which all living things on Earth depend.

.... (1)

(b) List **three** environmental factors which affect the speed at which microbes bring about decay.

1. ....

2. ....

3. .... (3)

Study the information below and answer questions (c) (i) to (iv).

The figure below shows the change in population of deer living on a plateau in Arizona.

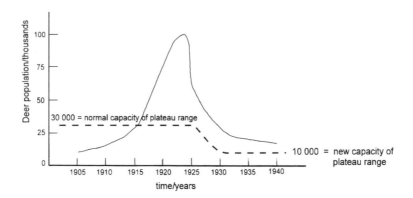

Between 1906 and 1923 thousands of predators of the deer such as wolves were killed by wildlife managers.

(c) (i) What was the normal capacity of the plateau between 1905 and 1926?

....deer   (1)

(ii) Suggest what the term normal capacity means here.

....   (1)

(iii) In which year was the deer population at the normal capacity for the plateau?

....   (1)

(iv) How did the size of the deer population change between 1907 and 1924? Suggest an explanation for this change.

....

....   (2)

MEG 1995

3. The table below shows some animals and examples of the food they eat.

Animal	lacewing fly	small bird	fox	weasel	vole	hawk
Food the animal eats	greenfly	lacewing fly, caterpillars	small birds, voles	voles	plants	small birds

(a) Complete the boxes A, B, C and D in the food web with names of animals from the table.

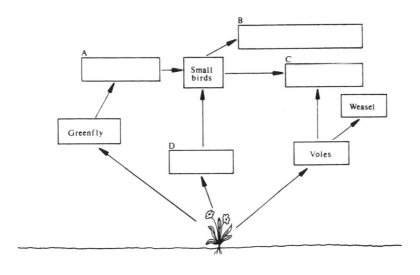

(4)

(b) Underline the word which describes the plant in the food web.

DECOMPOSER, PRODUCER, HERBIVORE, CARNIVORE (1)

(c) (i) Where does the energy for this food web come from?

.... (1)

(ii) Name the process which makes this energy available to plants.

.... (1)

(d) What might happen to the weasels and the plants if all the voles died?

Weasels: .... (1)

Plants: .... (1)

(e) A stoat is an animal which looks like a weasel and eats similar food.
Suggest and explain the change in the population of one named animal in the food web if stoats were released in the area.

Animal

....

Change

....

.... (3)

Edexcel 1995

4 (a) The diagram shows three possible pathways by which the energy captured by green plants may be passed onto humans.

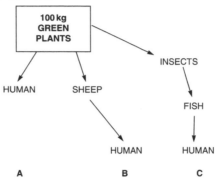

(i) Which of the pathways **A**, **B** or **C** would allow **most** energy from the plants to be available to humans? Explain your answer.

....

.... (2)

(ii) Which of the pathways **A**, **B** or **C** would be typical of starving populations? Explain your answer.

....

.... (2)

(iii) In which of the pathways **A**, **B** or **C** is most energy lost as heat? Explain your answer.

....

....

.... (2)

(b) (i) Look at the following food chain:

rose bush → aphids (greenflies) → ladybirds

Explain why the pyramid of **biomass** for this food chain would be a different shape from the pyramid of **numbers**.

....

....

.... (2)

(ii) The graph shows how the numbers of greenfly and ladybirds fluctuated over the Summer period during a year in which two of the weeks in July were hot and humid. This resulted in an abnormally high population of greenfly.

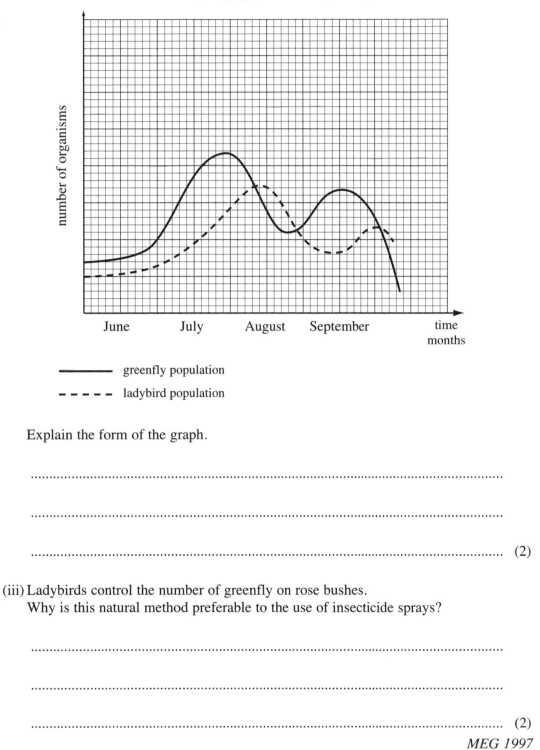

——————— greenfly population

– – – – – ladybird population

Explain the form of the graph.

....

....

.... (2)

(iii) Ladybirds control the number of greenfly on rose bushes.
Why is this natural method preferable to the use of insecticide sprays?

....

....

.... (2)

MEG 1997

5 Microbes and mankind

Most microbes are not harmful to mankind. Some are essential to maintain life as we know it, and others are exploited by us in biotechnology when they are used in the production of various foods, ethanol, antibiotics, and biogas.

Essential microbes

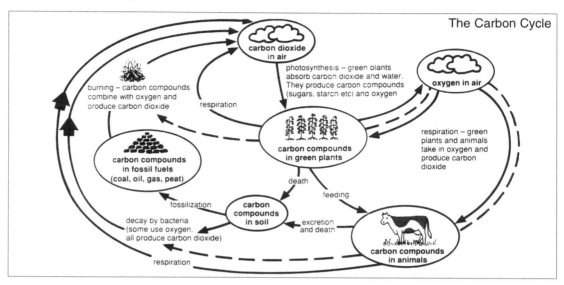

The Carbon Cycle

Carbon dioxide is taken from the environment by green plants during photosynthesis. The carbon is used to make carbohydrates, lipids (fats), and proteins. When these plants are eaten, the carbon enters the food chain. Some of the carbon becomes carbon dioxide during respiration and is returned to the environment.

When organisms die, microbes feed on them and carbon dioxide is released as carbon dioxide as the microbes respire. The recycling of carbon is called the **carbon cycle**.

In order to be able to make proteins, plants must also obtain nitrogen as nitrates by way of their roots. When microbes break down the waste products of animals and the protein in dead organisms, they make ammonium compounds.

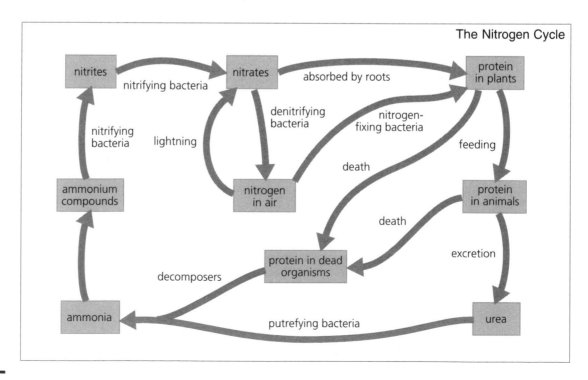

The Nitrogen Cycle

Nitrifying bacteria change ammonium compounds into a form that can be used by plants. **Nitrogen-fixing bacteria** living in the roots of certain plants can change nitrogen from the air into a form that can be used by plants. **Denitrifying bacteria** can replace nitrogen in the air by breaking down nitrates.

This constant recycling of nitrogen is called the nitrogen cycle. Without it, the world supply of protein would stop.

Microbes and biotechnology

Biotechnology uses **microbes** to make substances for us or to do work for us.

Certain types of bacteria are used in the production of some foods.

In the production of yoghurt, bacteria are added to milk at 30°C. The bacteria ferment the milk sugar, producing **lactic acid**. This causes the milk protein to become solid.

The single-celled fungus, yeast, can respire without oxygen, fermenting sugar to produce ethanol and carbon dioxide. In baking bread, a mixture of yeast and sugar is mixed with dough (flour and water). The mixture is left in a warm place to allow the yeast to respire rapidly. The carbon dioxide produced makes the bread rise. The bread is then baked in an oven.

In the production of the **antibiotic**, penicillin, a culture of the fungus, *Penicillium*, is added to a solution containing sugar in a large vessel called a fermenter. During the first 24 hours, the fungus rapidly grows. When the sugar in the medium becomes less, the fungus begins to produce penicillin. After 7 days, the medium is filtered and the penicillin removed.

Biogas, mainly methane, is produced by **anaerobic fermentation** of organic matter by microbes. Biogas production can be on a large scale so that it can be used as a fuel.

Ethanol-based fuels can be produced by the anaerobic fermentation of extracts of sugar cane with the use of yeast. Ethanol is distilled from the products and the resulting liquid can be used as fuel in motor vehicles.

Harmful microbes

Disease-causing microbes are called **pathogens** and include: viruses, bacteria, fungi, and single-celled animals called protozoa. Depending on the type, they can be spread through the air, by direct contact, through food and water, and by carriers such as insects.

The body has natural defence mechanisms including natural **immunity**. Artificial immunity may be acquired through vaccination.

A **vaccine** contains **antigens** derived from a pathogen. They cause the blood to produce **antibodies** which protect against infection by any future invasion by the pathogen. There are five common ways of producing a vaccine:

- using the killed pathogen, e.g. whooping cough;
- using a live weakened (attenuated) strain of the pathogen, e.g. tuberculosis, rubella;
- chemically modifying a toxic (poison) molecule so that it is no longer poisonous but still resembles the shape of the toxic molecule, e.g. diphtheria and tetanus;
- separating antigens from the microbe and using them as a vaccine, e.g. influenza;
- using genetically engineered bacteria to mass produce antigens, e.g. hepatitis B.

> **If you need to revise this subject more thoroughly, see the relevant topics in the *Letts* GCSE Biology Study Guide or CD-ROM.**

1   The diagram below shows part of the nitrogen cycle.

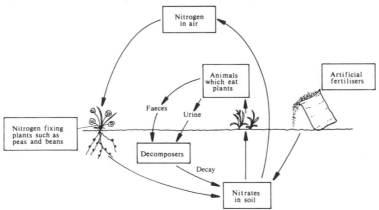

(a) (i)   What is meant by the term **decay?**

....

....

.... (2)

(ii) Name a type of organism which causes decay.

.... (1)

(b) What is meant by the term **nitrification**?

....

....

.... (2)

(c) The process of denitrification is shown but not named on the diagram. What is the end product of denitrification?

.... (1)

(d) Organic farmers do not use artificial fertilisers to put nitrates into the soil.

(i)   Explain why organic farmers often grow more peas and beans than other farmers.

....

....

.... (2)

(ii) Explain why **organic** farmers often keep farm animals even if they mainly grow crops such as wheat.

....

.... (1)

Edexcel 1995

2 Some students investigated the production of alcohol from sugars by yeast. They used solutions of the same concentration of four different sugars, **P, Q, R,** and **S**. For each sugar they set up the apparatus as in diagram **A**. The length of the bubble of carbon dioxide shown in diagram **B** was measured every five minutes for each apparatus. The temperature was kept at 25°C. The amount of carbon dioxide indicates the amount of alcohol produced.

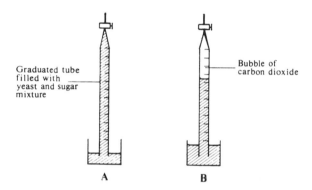

Graduated tube filled with yeast and sugar mixture

Bubble of carbon dioxide

A   B

The table below shows the results of the investigation.

Mixture	Length of CO$_2$ bubble at 5 minute intervals (cm)						
	5 mins	10 mins	15 mins	20 mins	25 mins	30 mins	35 mins
Yeast + Sugar P	3.0	10.0	17.0	26.0	35.0	38.0	40.0
Yeast + Sugar Q	0.5	1.0	1.5	2.0	2.0	2.0	2.0
Yeast + Sugar R	0.5	1.0	1.0	1.5	1.5	1.5	1.5
Yeast + Sugar S	4.0	11.0	19.0	27.0	36.0	40.0	42.0
Yeast + Water	0.5	0.5	0.5	1.0	1.0	1.0	1.0

(a) (i) Why was the yeast and water mixture included in the experiment?

.... (1)

(ii) Which sugar produced most alcohol?

.... (1)

(iii) Why was it important that the tubes were **completely** filled with the yeast and sugar mixture at the start of the experiment?

.... (1)

(iv) Why did the rate of production of carbon dioxide slow down after a time?

.... (1)

(b) Suggest **two** ways in which the rate of alcohol production could have been increased.

1...

2... (2)

(c) Yeast lives naturally on fruit. Some of the sugars (P, Q, R and S) came from animals. Suggest which of these sugars came from animals. Give a reason for your answer

....

....

.... (2)

Edexcel 1995

3 The diagram shows a sewage treatment plant.

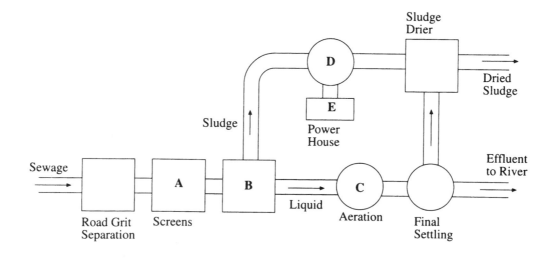

(a) (i) Suggest the function of the screens at **A**.

....

.... (1)

(ii) Outline what occurs at:

B ....

....

C ....

....

D ....

.... (3)

(b) (i) What passes from D to E?

.... (1)

(ii) What may happen to the sludge when it is removed from the treatment plant?

....

.... (1)

(c) Some bacteria in a sewage treatment plant change ammonium compounds to nitrates. What type are they?

.... (1)

(d) **Explain** what would happen to the water in a lake if untreated sewage enters it.

....

....

....

.... (2)

WJEC 1996

Water relations in plants

Water is the most important factor in a flowering plant's environment. The amount of water in an environment is critical in determining what types of plants will survive there.

Plants need water for almost all of the processes that go on inside them.

In photosynthesis, water supplies the hydrogen that combines with carbon dioxide to form carbohydrates. Water also plays a key role in providing a solvent for materials in cytoplasm of cells.

Also, water is the medium of transport of materials in plants. Manufactured foods and minerals, from the soil, are dissolved in water to be carried up and down in the **xylem** and **phloem**. Finally, water in the vacuoles of cells make them firm as a result of turgor pressure. This helps support non-woody plants.

Water balance in plants

In order to survive, an organism must remain in a state of balance with its environment. An important factor for this balance is the movement of materials in and out of cells. All of these materials must pass through the cell membrane.

The cell membrane is **selectively permeable**, i.e. different molecules and ions pass through it in different amounts and at different rates. Foods, water, wastes and other materials selectively pass through the membrane. Cytoplasm and stored foods are retained within the membrane.

Diffusion controls the movement of many molecules through the membrane and may be described as the spreading out of molecules from a region of greater concentration to one of lesser concentration. Diffusion of water is called **osmosis** and is the spreading of water molecules through a selectively permeable membrane from a region of greater concentration of water molecules to one of lesser concentration. When concentrations are the same on both sides of the selectively permeable membrane, the rate of movement of water molecules is equal in both directions. This is dynamic equilibrium.

In some cases, plants absorb mineral ions against the force of diffusion. Energy is used in this process, which is called **active transport**. Large molecules cannot pass through selectively permeable membranes. Instead, they flow into pouches in the membrane and are sealed off. They then enter the cell in vacuoles.

Transpiration

Water sometimes has to rise great distances through the stem. The most important forces that cause this are transpiration and cohesion of water molecules in the very narrow xylem vessels. Transpiration is water loss by evaporation from leaves and stems, mainly through pores called **stomata**. As the plant loses water through its stomata, it takes in water through the roots by osmosis. The entire column of water in the xylem is pulled up the stem by evaporation. On warm days, the transpiration rate is high because it depends on the same factors as evaporation. Stomata open during the day and close during the night or when there is a shortage of water.

During the day, photosynthesis take place in the **guard cells** of the stomata.

This produces glucose which dissolves in the cells' vacuoles. There is now relatively more water in the surrounding cells than in the guard

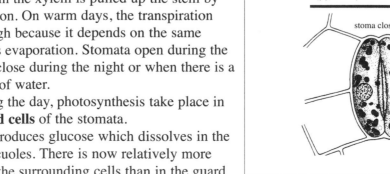

Stomata of a flowering plant

cells so the guard cells take in water by osmosis and swell, thus opening the pore. At night, no photosynthesis takes place, so there is no net flow of water into the guard cells and the pore closes.

Plant hormones

Hormones are of major importance in regulating the way that a plant grows. There are many groups of plant hormones, such as **auxins** and **gibberellins**.

Plants respond to their surroundings by growing either toward a stimulus (positive tropism) or away from one (negative tropism). This is done according to the hormonal effect on the growth of certain cells. Hormonal action is also affected by light and temperature changes. Commercial plant growers can control flowering and fruit ripening by means of artificial periods of light and darkness, as well as by application of certain hormones.

Limiting factors and photosynthesis

A limiting factor is one that governs the rate of a reaction by being above or below a certain critical level. An increase in such a factor will cause an increase in the rate of reaction, and a decrease in the factor will decrease the rate of the reaction.

Some limiting factors for photosynthesis are:

- Light
- Carbon dioxide
- Chlorophyll.

Each of these three factors can be investigated experimentally to prove that it is needed. By altering light intensity while keeping all other factors constant it is possible to show that an increase in light up to a maximum intensity will increase the rate of photosynthesis. Once the maximum intensity has been reached, damage to chlorophyll will occur and the rate will slow down. Similarly, an increase in the concentration of carbon dioxide, up to maximum, will increase the rate of photosynthesis. Once the maximum has been reached, the carbon dioxide alters the acidity of the plant's cells and the rate of photosynthesis will decrease.

Plants containing the green pigment, chlorophyll, are able to capture light energy for photosynthesis (see page 7). Some plants are not green but still capture light energy, e.g. red and brown seaweeds and ornamental plants with varicoloured (variegated) leaves. They contain chlorophyll but it is hidden by the other pigments.

Chlorophyll is packaged into containers in cells called chloroplasts They are very tiny and are usually disc-shaped structures in some cells exposed to light in leaves and stems. Leaves are particularly well adapted to trap energy so that they can act as centres for photosynthesis.

Adaptations of leaves for photosynthesis

❶ Large surface area so that the leaf traps the maximum amount of light energy and absorbs the maximum amount of carbon dioxide.

❷ Very thin so that no one cell is far from the light source.

❸ Cells allow light penetration.

❹ Chlorophyll distribution in chloroplasts near to the upper surface of the leaf.

❺ Leaf position arranged so that it receives the maximum amount of light without overshadowing.

❻ Holes (stomata) in the leaf allow exchange of gases.

❼ Spaces between cells to allow the movement of gases.

❽ Well developed supply system to carry water and salts to the cells. Distribution system to export food from the leaf.

If you need to revise this subject more thoroughly, see the relevant topics in the *Letts* GCSE *Biology Study Guide* or *CD-ROM*.

1 The diagrams show the details of an experiment with an auxin.

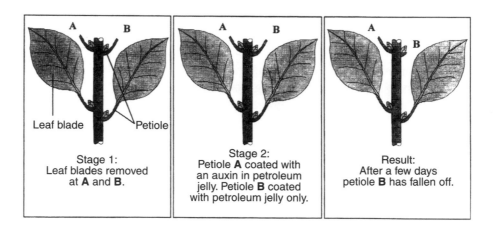

Stage 1:
Leaf blades removed
at **A** and **B**.

Stage 2:
Petiole **A** coated with
an auxin in petroleum
jelly. Petiole **B** coated
with petroleum jelly only.

Result:
After a few days
petiole **B** has fallen off.

(a) Why was petiole **B** covered in petroleum jelly that did not contain an auxin?

....

.... (1)

(b) Using the information from the experiment, explain how leaf-fall might be controlled by the plant.

....

....

.... (2)

(c) When a gardener removes the shoot tip of a shrub, side branches start to grow out from the main stem. Explain why this happens.

....

....

....

.... (2)

SEG 1998

2 The graph shows the water loss from a plant during a hot windy day.

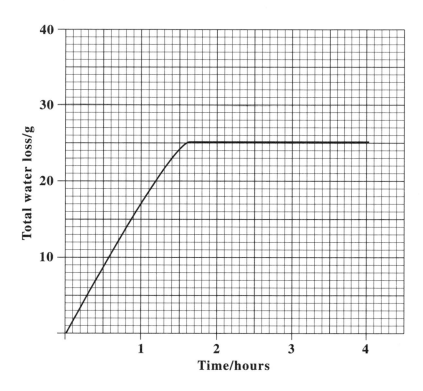

(a) Explain how the plant loses water.

....

....

....

.... (2)

(b) Explain why the plant might wilt two hours after the start of the experiment on a hot windy day.

....

....

....

.... (2)

(c) Draw a curve on the graph showing the water loss of the same plant during a hot humid day. (2)

NICCEA 1995

3 The table shows the results of an investigation in which small pieces of potato were placed in different concentrations of sugar solution.

% Concentration sugar solution	% Change in mass of potato
5	+8
10	+3
15	+1
20	-8
25	-11

Note that + means a mass increase and - means a mass decrease.

(a) Estimate the % concentration of sugar solution that would produce a 5% loss in mass.

.... (1)

(b) What concentration of sugar is closest to the concentration of the potato cell sap ?

.... (1)

(c) Name the biological process which would cause the loss or gain in mass.

.... (1)

(d) State two examples of the process in living organisms.

(i) ....

(ii) .... (2)

(e) Explain why some pieces of potato lost mass whereas others gained mass.

....

....

....

....

....

.... (4)

4 Four different potted plants. **A**, **B**, **C** and **D**, of the same species were used in an investigation.

Plant A was a variegated variety i.e. leaves with both green and non-green areas. The other plants were all of a non-variegated green variety. Plant B had been grown entirely in the dark. All four plants were placed in a dark cupboard for 48 hours. A starch test on a leaf taken from each of the plants A, B, C and D showed negative results.

Four test tubes labelled A, B, C and D were partly filled with the same amount of orange-coloured hydrogencarbonate indicator solution (HCIS). A second leaf from each of the four plants was then placed in the appropriate test tube. The four leaves were approximately the same size. The test tubes were set up as shown below and were placed at equal distances from a bright light source for six hours.

HCIS containing an atmospheric concentration of carbon dioxide is orange-red in colour. At high carbon dioxide concentration it goes yellow. Lowering the dissolved carbon dioxide concentration results in a colour change from yellow to a purple-red/claret.

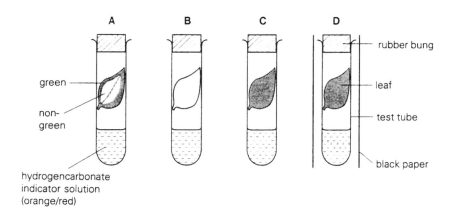

(a) The table shows the colour of the HCIS in each test tube at the end of the six hour period.

A	B	C	D
red	yellow	purple-red/claret	yellow

(i) Name the carbon dioxide absorbing process which occurs in leaf **C** but not in **D** and explain why the process does not happen in **D**.

....

....

.... (2)

(ii) Name another process which occurs in the leaves in both test tubes C and D and which causes the colour change in D. Why does the colour change occur?

....

....

.... (4)

(iii) Explain the difference in colour of the HCIS in test tubes A and C.

....

....

....

....

....

.... (4)

(b) After the six hours exposure to light, the leaves were taken from the test tube and tested for starch using iodine solution.

(i) The diagrams show the leaves after the starch test. Shade the leaves where appropriate to show the expected results.

A   B   C   D

(2)

(ii) Explain the results you have shown for leaf **B**.

....

....

....

.... (3)

(c) What is the importance of the negative results obtained when testing the leaves for starch immediately after the plants had been in the dark for 48 hours?

....

....

....

.... (2)

MEG 1996

5 The diagram shows the lower part of a section through the leaf of a flowering plant.

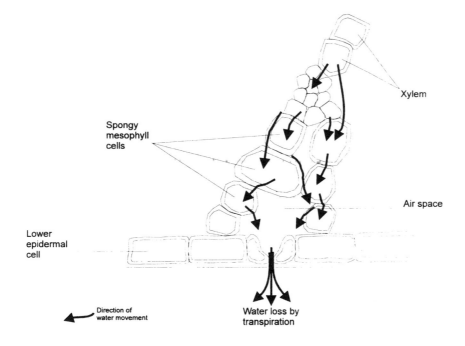

(a) (i) Not all of the water entering the leaf through the xylem is transpired through the stomata of the leaf. What happens to the water not transpired through the stomata?

....

....

.... (2)

(ii) Describe briefly how you could show that the water present in the xylem is the same water that was absorbed by the roots of the plant.

....

....

....

....

.... (3)

(iii) Name the support material, other than cellulose, present in the walls of the xylem vessels.

.... (1)

(iv) The cell walls of the spongy mesophyll cells are little more than thin layers of cellulose. Describe how these cells support the leaf.

....

....

....

.... (2)

(v) Describe how the loss of water vapour through the stomata contributes to the transport of materials from the roots to the leaves.

....

....

....

.... (2)

(b) The graph shows the relative size of the stomatal openings over a 24-hour period for a flowering plant growing in a temperate climate in early Summer.

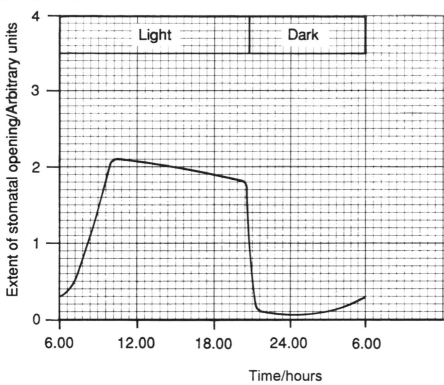

(i) Using the data in the graph above, describe what happens to the stomatal openings during the 24-hour period.

....

....

....

....

....

....

....

....

.... (5)

(ii) In temperate regions, temporary closure of the stomata may happen occasionally during daylight hours. Suggest an explanation for this fact.

....

....

....

.... (2)

(iii) In the tropics, closure of stomata for a period around midday is very common. State one disadvantage and one advantage to the plant of this behaviour.

Disadvantage ....

....

Advantage ....

.... (2)

(iv) Describe how osmosis may be involved in controlling the opening and closing of stomata.

....

....

....

....

....

....

....

....

....

....

.... (5)

MEG 1995

*Try to complete this paper in a single sitting of **1 hour**.*

1 The graph shows Kelvin's daily temperature whilst suffering from a bacterial disease.

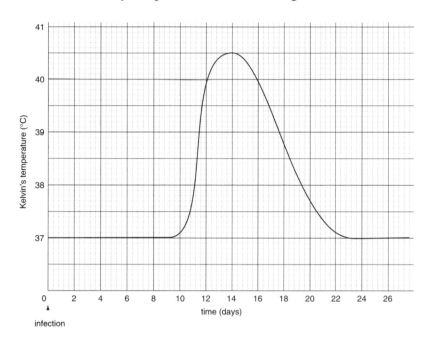

(a) Use the graph to help you answer these questions.
  (i) What was Kelvin's normal body temperature? .... (1)

  (ii) What was Kelvin's highest temperature recorded? .... (1)

(b) (i) How many days was the incubation period?... (1)

  (ii) Describe what was happening inside the patients body during the incubation period.

  .... (1)

(c) (i) Write down a reason for the increase in body temperature.

  .... (1)

  (ii) The increase in body temperature is a symptom of a bacterial infection.
  Suggest **two** other symptoms that usually occur with a bacterial infection.

  ....

  .... (2)

(d) (i) Kelvin was told to stay at home as his condition was infectious.

What is meant by infectious? ....

.... (1)

(ii) Suggest four ways in which germs can spread.

1. ....

2. ....

3. ....

4. .... (4)

(e) Kelvin's infection was due to bacteria. Some of these statements describe bacteria and some describe viruses.
List the statement letter under the correct heading. The first one has been done for you.

A are microbes
B can only live inside other cells
C can be treated with antibiotics
D made up of a protein core containing a few genes
E these cells can be seen through a microscope

bacteria ......A..

viruses .... (4)

2 The table gives some information about foods and their use in the body.
Complete the table.

food type	food sources	use in body
	sugar, cakes, bread	
protein		
	butter, margarine, cooking oil	Insulate the body and as a store of energy
	fresh fruit and vegetables	essential for good health

(6)

3 The diagram shows information about living things in a lake.

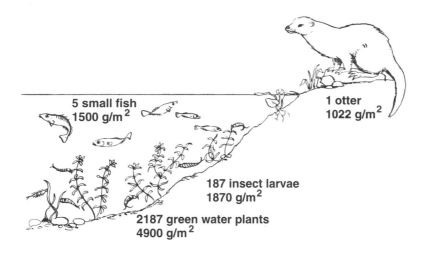

5 small fish
1500 g/m^2

1 otter
1022 g/m^2

187 insect larvae
1870 g/m^2

2187 green water plants
4900 g/m^2

(a) Use the information shown in this diagram to help you answer the questions.
   (i) Draw the food chain shown in the diagram.

(1)

   (ii) Draw and label a pyramid of biomass to represent this food chain.

(3)

   (iii) A disease killed all of the insect larvae in the lake.
        Describe the effect this would have on the other living things in the lake.

   ....

   .... (2)

(b) A farmer spread fertiliser on the fields surrounding the lake.
    A few months later dead fish were found in the lake.
    Explain what happened to cause the death of the fish.

   ....

   ....

   ....

   .... (4)

QUESTIONS

4 (a) The diagram shows the structure of a leaf. Finish labelling the diagram.
    (i) Choose the best words from this list: **cuticle**, **lower epidermis**, **palisade layer**, **spongy layer**, **stomata**, **upper epidermis**.

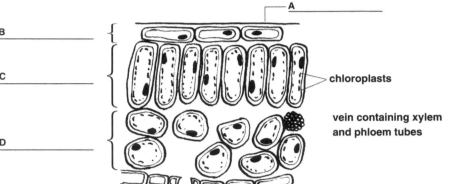

(4)

(ii) Describe the function of the xylem and phloem tubes.

Xylem tubes ....

....

Phloem tubes...

.... (2)

(iii) Describe the function of the stomata.

....

.... (2)

(iv) Explain why there are so many air spaces in the lower layer of cells.

.... (1)

These features aid photosynthesis.
(v) Suggest other ways that the leaf is adapted for photosynthesis.

....

....

....

.... (4)

(vi) Complete the symbol equation for photosynthesis.

$$. \ .... + ... \xrightarrow[\text{chlorophyll}]{\text{light}} C_6H_{12}O_6 + ...$$ (2)

(b) An experiment was set up to measure the amount of oxygen given off during photosynthesis.

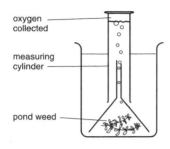

The experiment was repeated with different light intensities.
The amount of oxygen collected was recorded every ten minutes.
The results are plotted on the graph.

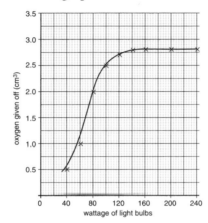

(i) Use the results shown on the graph to explain how light intensity affects the rate of photosynthesis.

....

.... (2)

Sodium hydrogen carbonate was added to the water, this provided extra carbon dioxide for the pond weed. The experiment was repeated and the results recorded.

Wattage of light bulb (W)	oxygen given off (cm^3)
40	0.8
60	1.5
80	2.5
100	3.0
120	3.2
140	3.3
160	3.4
180	3.4
200	3.4
220	3.4

(ii) Plot these results on the graph above. (2)

(iii) Finish the graph by drawing the best curve. (1)

5 The diagram shows the structure of human skin.
   (a) Finish labelling the diagram. Choose the best words from this list.
       blood, **vessel**, **hair**, **muscle**, **nerve**, **sebaceous gland**, **sweat gland**.

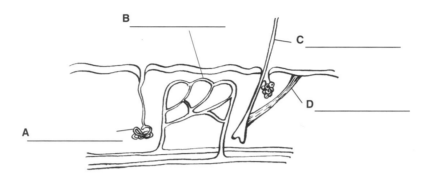

(4)

The skin helps to maintain a constant body temperature.
(b) (i) Explain how the structures in the skin help to maintain a constant body temperature
        during cold weather.

....

....

.... (4)

   (ii) Explain how the process of sweating removes heat from our bodies.

.... (1)

Answers

1 LIFE PROCESSES

Question	Answer	Mark

1 (a) (i)

Part of digestive system	Letter
Liver	**H**
Pancreas	**C**
Oesophagus	**A**
Appendix	**G**

4

(ii) E is the colon and has the function of absorbing water from the indigestible material that it contains. **1**

(iii) 1. Large surface area provided by villi. 2. Good blood supply. (or A thin lining. Lacteals for digested fat absorption.) **2**

(One mark each)

(b) (i)

Other tissues

Muscle

Fat (storage)

Fat (essential)

Bone

2

(ii) Muscle. (iii) Female. (iv) $\frac{45}{100} \times 80 = 36\,\text{kg}$. 1 mark for each **3**

2 (a) (i) Amylase. (ii) Salivary glands or pancreas. 1 mark for each **2**

(b) (i) An enzyme will have its own optimum pH for its action to proceed at the fastest rate. A pH above or below this optimum, will reduce the rate of the enzyme's action. **1**

(ii)

	Statement numbers
The enzyme pepsin acts only on protein molecules.	1, 3
Protein molecules are broken down to form short chains of amino acids.	1, 5

2

Letts

Q&A

Question	Answer	Mark

3 (a)

Name	Function
Ligament	Holds the bones of a joint together
Cartilage	Reduces friction between bones at a joint
Synovial fluid	Lubricates the joint to reduce friction.

2

(b) Two muscles are needed to control movements of the bones of a hinge joint because they work in antagonistic pairs. **1**
While one is contracting, its partner is relaxing. **1**

> **Examiner's tip** A common confusion is between a ligament and a tendon. Remember that a tendon connects a muscle to a bone. It will not be sufficient just to mention that muscles act in antagonistic pairs. For both marks, you will need to explain the meaning of the term.

4 (a) (i) The palisade layer. **1**

(ii) The upper epidermis. **1**

(b) The air spaces allow air with carbon dioxide to circulate throughout the leaf. **1**
They enable a large surface area to be present for gaseous exchange. **1**
They keep the air saturated to keep a moist surface area for gaseous exchange. **1**

> **Examiner's tip** Part (a) relies on simple observation but part (b) requires knowledge of the features of an efficient surface for gaseous exchange. These are principles which apply to all such surfaces whether they are for breathing or photosynthesis.

5 (a) The pancreas **1**

(b) Diabetes **1**

(c) The pancreas must be able to produce insulin when it is needed.
The effects of injections of insulin soon wear off. **1**

(d) (i) The antibodies would react with insulin (because it is a protein like an antigen). **1**

(ii) The white blood cells would ingest (engulf) the insulin-secreting cells. **1**

(e) Insulin helps to regulate glucose. **1**
Insulin removes glucose from the blood. **1**
Glucagon helps to change glycogen into glucose. **1**

(f) Correct order is C, D, B, E, A. **5 x 1**

(g) It can be made in large quantities. It does not involve the killing of animals.
Any one for 1 mark.

Question	Answer	Mark

Examiner's tip The question brings together three areas of your syllabus i.e. knowledge of blood sugar regulation, antibody – antigen reactions, and genetic engineering.
At this higher level, note that a complete coverage of the syllabus is essential. The temptation to concentrate on a limited number of topics must be resisted. Note that for part (e) it is easy to confuse glucagon with glycogen.
Also, note that part (f) carries 5 marks for a correct sequence of events. A thorough knowledge of the principles of genetic engineering is needed or almost all of the five marks will be lost.

Question	Answer	Mark
6 (a)	Any two of: It has long/pointed horns for defence. It has long legs to run away. It has long legs to kick predators. It is tall and can see predators a long distance away. Its eyes are on the side of its head to see predators. It has large ears to hear predators approaching. It has markings for camouflage.	2
(b) (i)	It falls in the morning/day and rises at night.	1
(ii)	There is loss due to evaporation or transpiration in the day. It is absorbed from the air at night/when cool.	1
(c) (i)	20:30 and 08:00.	1
(ii)	Any two of: There is the highest moisture content in grass. It needs water in desert conditions. There is less chance of predation.	2
(d) (i)	Water loss is reduced.	1
(ii)	There is evaporation of water which uses energy or heat.	1
	There is a large surface area of blood vessels for evaporation or radiation.	1
(iii)	There is a large surface area of blood vessels.	1
	The cool blood in veins cools the blood in arteries.	1

Examiner's tip Note that in part (a) there are many alternatives but a mention of just strong or powerful legs would not gain credit. Also note that in order to gain maximum credit for part (a) both the advantageous structure and its function must be mentioned. In part (b) both points must be made in (i) and (ii) for full credit. The whole question tests observation and deduction rather than recall.

2 INHERITANCE AND EVOLUTION

Question	Answer	Mark
1 (a)	Hormones are chemical secretions of ductless glands.	1
	producing a definite physiological effect in the body.	1
(b) (i)	It is 'cut' out using enzymes.	1
(ii)	[A] A clone is a group of genetically identical organisms or cells derived from a single individual by asexual reproduction.	1
		1
	[B] They reproduce asexually	1
	very rapidly.	1

Question	Answer	Mark
	Bacteria can be cultured using cheap waste materials from industrial food manufacture.	1
(c)	It does not involve killing animals.	1
	There are many people whose cultural beliefs do not allow or agree with killing animals for human benefit.	1
	OR Because of mass production	1
	supply will keep up with demand.	1

> **Examiner's tip**
> (a) Note the importance of a concise definition here. Most candidates would have a knowledge of certain hormones and their effects, but it is not so easy to write a definition which applies to all animal produced hormones. NOT ALL hormones are concerned with growth and development.
> (b)(ii)[A] Again, a definition is needed. Two marks are available – 'genetically identical' and 'asexual reproduction' are the important points.
> [B] Do not fall into the trap of writing about the ethics of using animal-derived insulin here. There is scope for this in part (c).

Question	Answer	Mark
2 (a)	Dominant S Recessive s	1
(b)	Genotypes Ss X ss	1+1
(c)	Correct gametes: 1 mark, method: 1 mark	2
(d) (i)	Any three of:	
	The importance of camouflage.	
	The best adapted survived to breed/pass on genes.	
	The environment changed.	
	There was predation on the snails that were visible.	3
(ii)	The mutation rate was affected because of radiation.	2

For (b):

	s	s
S	Ss	Ss
s	ss	ss

For (c):

	S	s
S	SS	Ss
s	sS	ss

> **Examiner's tip**
> It is important to have a thorough understanding of the terms dominant, recessive and genotype. Also you must know the correct procedure for assigning symbols to genotypes in genetic problems. Remember the recessive allele is always shown by a lower case equivalent of the capital letter that represents the dominant character. In (d) the example shows natural selection at work and even though you might not have studied this particular example the same principle applies to the examples stated in the syllabus that you are studying.

Question	Answer	Mark
3 (a)	C	1
(b)	Male	1
	blue eyes	1
(c) (i)	**bb**	1
(ii)	The gene for blue eyes is recessive. If Sarah had the B genes, she would have brown eyes.	1
(d) (i)	Lucy	1
(ii)	In order to be an identical twin to Rachel, the twin must be female and have the same genotype.	1, 1

Question	Answer	Mark

4 (a) (i) The transfer of pollen from the anther to the stigma of a different flower of the same species.

1
1

(ii) Because the parents were pure-bred (both homozygous) Red is dominant to white.

1
1

(iii) Key: **R** = red (dominant). **r** = white (recessive)

1
(for key)

Parents	Genotypes	**Rr** x	**Rr**

1
(for genotypes)

Phenotypes   Red   Red

1
(for phenotypes)

Gametes   **R + r**   **R + r**

1
(for gametes)

F2

	R	r
R	RR red	Rr red
r	rR red	rr white

1
(for working)

F2 ratio   3 red to 1 white

1

(b) (i) A mutation is a change in genetic makeup resulting in a new characteristic that can be inherited.

1

Here, a mutation of DNA could have taken place by the wrong pattern of base pairs being produced when DNA duplicated itself (replication).

1

DNA regulates the production of colour in the flower.

1

(ii) The blue colour was an advantage to the species.

1

More pollinating insects could have been attracted to the blue colour than the red for pollination.

1

Reproduction would ensure that the gene was passed on to future generations.

1

3 POPULATIONS AND HUMAN INFLUENCES

Question	Answer	Mark
1 (a) (i)	There is a higher percentage of the population between 0 and 5 years in Honduras than in Sweden.	1
(ii)	There is a higher percentage of people alive after 10 years in Sweden than in Honduras.	2
(b)	The factors could be any two of the following: Poor medical care, poor diet, disease, poor housing, unemployment, quality of water. The explanations are: There would be a greater death rate from complications resulting at birth if poor medical care was available. Poor diet would lead to malnutrition or starvation in early years. Infectious diseases would endanger the lives of children who had no immunity. Poor housing could lead to over-crowding and spread of diseases. Unemployment could lead to poverty and the inability to provide a healthy diet. The quality of water is important because of possible contamination by disease-causing microbes.	4

Examiner's tip Here is a typical example of how you can gain marks by interpretation of data. It is important to be able to understand such 'population pyramids'. Note that in part (b), you will gain full marks only if you state two factors and give explanations of each of them. Just to mention the factors will not be enough.

Question	Answer	Mark
2 (a) (i)	Photosynthesis	1
(ii)	Respiration or decay.	1
(iii)	Coal	1
(iv)	Road transport.	1

Examiner's tip The examiner would never write a 'trick question'. Do not be put off if the answer seems obvious.

Question	Answer	Mark
(b) (i)	The Greenhouse Effect.	1
(ii)	Large amounts of carbon dioxide (and other greenhouse gases) are trapped under the ozone layer.	1
	The sun's rays (short-wave solar radiation) enter the Earth's atmosphere. Some of this is absorbed by the Earth.	1
	Long-wave radiation is reflected back towards space but is reflected back down to Earth by the greenhouse gases.	1
	This causes a heating up of the Earth's surface.	1

Question	Answer	Mark

3 (a) (i) 2 marks for correct plots and 1 for carefully drawn curve.   **3**

      (ii) The number of species of lichens increases.   **1**

      (iii) 10km   **1**
There is a decrease in the number of species of lichen   **1**
because of the sulphur dioxide produced by traffic.   **1**

   (b) (i) Lecanora   **1**
      (ii) Parmelia, Xanthoria and Lecanora   **1**

   (c) Bronchitis caused by irritation of the lungs by sulphur dioxide.   **1**

4 (a) It is a breeding site for birds.   **1**

   (b) Phosphates   **1**

   (c) The algae release poisonous chemicals when they die and decompose.   **1**

   (d) The woollen mill or sewage or run-off from farmland.   any 2 x **1**

   (e) By controlling housing development in the area.   **1**

   (f) (i) Run-off   **1**

      (ii) 18 kg/day   **1**

Question	Answer	Mark
5 (a)	The drought would evaporate the water and concentrate the lead.	1
(b)	The lead affected the nervous system	1
	which supplied the muscles of the trunk.	1
(c)	The lead would be concentrated through food chains	1
	and enter humans in the diet via fish.	1
(d)	Correct order from top to bottom is D, E, B, G.	4 × 1

Examiner's tip This is an example of a question which asks you to apply your knowledge of the effects of heavy metal poisoning to an unfamiliar situation. In order to prepare yourself for this type of question, it is essential to understand rather than learn by re-call. The context of the topic could be almost any situation where humans pollute the environment with heavy metals. However, note that a lot of information is given in the beginning of the question. This requires comprehension. For part (d), you are required to interpret data in the form of a graph. This is a very popular technique in setting questions on population changes.

4 ECOSYSTEMS

Question	Answer	Mark
1 (a)	Algae → Snails → Caddis larvae → Diving beetles OR	
	Pondweed → hog lice → Caddis larvae → Diving beetles OR	
	Algae → water fleas → Mussels → Mites	
	The marks are for: the correct sequence	1
	and direction of arrows.	1
(b) (i)	Light. Temperature. Number of herbivores. Mineral concentration.	4
	Number of carnivores (indirectly). 1 for each of any 4	
(ii)	Water fleas would increase	1
	because there would be more food for them.	1
	The mussels would increase	1
	because there would be more algae and waterfleas for them to eat.	1
(c)	2 loach / 30 snails / Algae	1 / 1
(d)	Oxygen is used by the animals and plants in respiration but is produced by plants in photosynthesis. Carbon dioxide is used by plants in photosynthesis but is produced by animals and plants during respiration.	1 / 1

Question	Answer	Mark

Part (a) is a very popular way of testing the understanding of food webs and food chains. It is essential to indicate the correct direction of the arrows because this is the only way that you can show the direction of energy flow. Part (b) requires an understanding of the feeding relationships within this community. It shows how the population of one species is dependent on another. (c) Note that you need to know how to translate the numerical data into a pyramid of number. Sometimes data is given so that you can make a pyramid of biomass. (Mass of living material per unit area or volume.) Finally, in part (d), there is opportunity to show how animals depend on plants and vice versa – the basic principle of ecology.

2 (a)   The Sun   **1**

   (b)   Temperature, pH, Water, oxygen   any 3 × **1**

   (c) (i) 30 000   **1**

       (ii) When the birth rate and death rate are equal or the maximum number of a species that can be supported in a given habitat without affecting the population of other species.   **1**

     (iii) 1915   **1**

     (iv) It rose gradually and then very sharply.   **1**
          The probable reason was that the predators were killed and the conditions for feeding and reproducing were favourable.   **1**

Predator-prey relationships provide plenty of data that examiners can use to set questions on this topic. Note that most of the answers require interpretation of graphical data in this case. The context may be unfamiliar, but the principles will be the same for any habitat.

3 (a)   A lacewing fly. B hawk or fox. C fox. D caterpillars.   4 × **1**

   (b)   <u>PRODUCER</u>

   (c) (i) Sunlight   **1**

       (ii) Photosynthesis   **1**

   (d)   The weasels would decrease in number.   **1**
          The plants would increase in number.   **1**

   (e)   The voles would decrease   **1**
          because there would be more predators   **1**
          which would compete with the weasels.   **1**

Part (a) requires careful interpretation of given data. At first, you might think that C could be a fox or a weasel but a careful consideration shows you that the weasel is already given in the food web. However, B has two alternatives according to the data in the table. Caterpillars for D have to be deduced from the data and not directly read from the table. The table shows that only voles eat plants. Parts (b) and (c) require knowledge but (d) and (e) test your skills at interpreting the given data.

Question	Answer	Mark
4 (a) (i)	A	1
	because there is only one link to allow energy loss between feeding levels.	1
(ii)	C	1
	because it would have the greatest energy loss and consequently least energy left to support the human population.	1
(iii)	B	1
	because more energy as heat would be lost in maintaining the constant body temperature of the mammals involved.	1
(b) (i)	Many insects can feed on one plant.	1
	The biomass of the plant is greater than the biomass of the insects.	1
(ii)	The peak for the predators (ladybirds) is slightly out of phase with that of their food (in July and August).	1
	The population of predators increases as the food increases but decreases when prey numbers decrease.	1
	OR emigration and immigration of ladybirds could explain their decrease and increase.	
	OR disease could have caused the decrease of either greenflies and ladybirds.	
(iii)	Insecticides can kill useful insects	1
	and they can cause environmental harm by building up in concentration through food chains and killing animals at the end of food chains.	1

> **Examiner's tip** (a) Although this question appears to assess skills of data handling, it actually requires a sound understanding of energy transfer and energy loss between links in food chains. It would be wise to revise the ways in which energy is lost between feeding levels. (b) This part cannot be answered without recall and understanding of the terms, biomass, and pyramids of numbers. Parts (ii) and (iii) are more open ended because the graph could be interpreted in a number of correct ways, all of which would be given credit by the examiner who set the question. The effects of insecticides are also varied, but the mark scheme will accommodate correct answers.

5 MICROBES AND MANKIND

Question	Answer	Mark
1 (a) (i)	Decay is the breakdown of organic material	1
	by microbes.	1
(ii)	Bacteria or Fungi	1
(b)	Nitrification is the build up of nitrites and nitrates from ammonium compounds,	1

Question		Answer	Mark
		by nitrifying bacteria.	1
(c)		Nitrogen	1
(d)	(i)	Peas and beans have nitrogen fixing bacteria in their roots.	1
		These can change nitrogen from the atmosphere into a form that can be used by plants.	1
	(ii)	They use the animals' excretory products as a source of nitrogen for the nitrogen cycle.	1

Examiner's tip Candidates often find the concept of the nitrogen cycle difficult. This may be because they try to learn the flow chart of the cycle without really understanding it. Questions will concentrate on the role of the bacteria involved in the cycle and this is no exception. It is useful to realise that there are four types of bacteria involved. These are: putrefying, nitrifying, nitrogen-fixing, and denitrifying. You should learn and understand the function of each type. The names of the species of bacteria are not required to be known.

2 (a)	(i)	As a control, to show that the sugar was responsible for carbon dioxide production.	1
	(ii)	Sugar S	1
	(iii)	To remove all the air and to have the same conditions at the start.	1
	(iv)	Because the sugar was used up.	1
(b)		Raise the temperature to the optimum for yeast.	1
		Replace sugar as it is being used.	1
(c)		Q and R.	1
		Yeasts do not naturally occur in animals and do not use sugars from animals for fermentation.	1

Examiner's tip This may be an unfamiliar experiment to you but it is really about principles of fermentation by yeast. Note that the concepts of a control and experimental procedure must be understood. The use of yeast in biotechnology is a popular topic for questions.

3 (a)	(i)	To remove any floating material.	1
	(ii)	**B** Settlement of sludge to the bottom of the liquid.	1
		C Killing harmful microbes by increasing oxygen via aeration.	1
		D Anaerobic digestion of sludge by microbes.	1
(b)	(i)	Methane	1
	(ii)	It is used as fertiliser on land.	1
(c)		Nitrifying bacteria	1
(d)		Sewage contains nitrates. These are used by plants for growth. There would be an overgrowth of plants.	

Question	Answer	Mark
	These plants would eventually die.	
	Bacteria would cause these to decay and so take oxygen from the water.	2

Examiner's tip Here is another example of biotechnology where microbes are used to do work for us. In this case it is the treatment of sewage. You are required to learn the details of the process. This is typical of questions to be expected on this topic. Note the examiner's attempt to test your knowledge of one effect of humans on the environment in part (d).Therefore, be prepared for questions which test a mixture of topics.

6 PLANT BIOLOGY

Question	Answer	Mark
1 (a)	It acts as a control. OR	
	It shows if anything other than auxin caused the effect.	1
(b)	The auxin keeps the petiole on the plant. OR	
	Lack of auxin causes the petiole to drop.	1
	There is a reduction in auxin levels.	1
(c)	Auxin prevents side shoots from growing. OR	
	When the auxin supply is stopped, side branches appear.	1
	Auxin is produced by the shoot tip.	1

Examiner's tip Note that for part (a) an unqualified reference to a fair test would not gain credit. The effects of hormones on the development of plants is on all biology syllabi. Here the concept is applied to the classical investigations into apical dominance. However it could just as easily be applied to phototropism or horticultural applications like fruit ripening or hormonal weed killers.

Question	Answer	Mark
2 (a)	Plants lose water because of evaporation	1
	through stomata and the cuticle of both stems and leaves.	1
(b)	Wilting occurs when the rate of water loss by evaporation exceeds	1
	the rate of water entry through the roots due to osmosis.	1
(c)	The curve should follow the shape of the one given but it should be	
	below the line shown	1
	and should level off in the same way.	1
3 (a)	Any number between 16 and 19.	1
(b)	15%	1

Question	Answer	Mark
(c)	Osmosis	1
(d)	The movement of water into roots.	1
	The movement of water into guard cells when stomata open.	1
	(OR the diffusion of water through the lining of the intestine in animals or the re-absorption of water in the kidney tubules.)	
(e)	The potato tissue would lose mass when water passed out from the cells,	1
	from where it was in relatively high concentration,	1
	to where it was in relatively low concentration;	1
	through the selectively permeable cell membrane.	1
	The same marks would be given for the opposite explanation when the potato gained mass.	

Examiner's tip Parts (a) and (b) require deduction from the data. The rest requires knowledge and understanding of the principles of diffusion and osmosis. Common errors in part (e) are descriptions of solutions (rather than water) passing through a selectively permeable membrane, and a statement that the cell wall (rather than the cell membrane) is selectively permeable.

Question	Answer	Mark
4 (a) (i)	Photosynthesis	1
	This process did not occur in D because light energy is required for photosynthesis to take place.	1

Examiner's tip In most experiments investigating photosynthesis, the usual variable to control is light.

(ii)	Respiration occurs in both C and D.	1
	Respiration produces carbon dioxide.	1
	As no photosynthesis is taking place no carbon dioxide is removed.	1
	In high carbon dioxide concentration HCIS turns yellow.	1

Examiner's tip You must ensure that you have your facts correct before you start to write down this answer. Read the information again, then plan your answer out in rough, and check that you have the 4 facts. Then write your answer out neatly.

(iii)	Leaf C has more chlorophyll than leaf A	1
	so more photosynthesis took place in leaf C.	1
	More photosynthesis requires more carbon dioxide to be absorbed,	1
	less carbon dioxide in C causes HCIS indicator to turn purple-red.	1

Examiner's tip Again check your 4 facts before you start to write your answer.

Question	Answer	Mark

(b) (i)

blue/black ——
brown ——

All four correctly shaded in.   **2**
(Only two or three shaded in correctly = 1 mark)
(Only one shaded correctly = 0 marks)

(ii) Plant B was kept in the dark so no chlorophyll developed,   **1**
this means photosynthesis was prevented,   **1**
therefore no starch was produced.   **1**

(c) This shows that the leaf did not contain any starch before
the experiment,   **1**
therefore any starch formed must have been produced by
photosynthesis during the experiment.   **1**
This made it a fair test or a control.   **1**

(Any two)

5 (a) (i) It is used for photosynthesis   **1**
and to maintain pressure in cell vacuoles for support.   **1**

(ii) Place a complete flowering plant (with roots attached) into a solution of
harmless coloured dye.   **1**
Leave it for a day.   **1**
Examine a section through the stem and note the presence of
the coloured dye in the xylem.   **1**

(iii) Lignin   **1**

(iv) Their vacuoles are filled with cell sap.   **1**
This provides pressure which supports the cells.   **1**

(v) The evaporation of water vapour through the stomata acts as a suction
which draws up water through the xylem.   **1**
This suction is transmitted through the stem to the roots.   **1**

Question		Answer	Mark
(b)	(i)	Between 6 a.m. and 11 a.m. the stomata open.	1
		They then start to close when the light is at its maximum.	1
		They close gradually until about 21.00 hrs	1
		and then very rapidly until 22.00 hrs.	1
		Most remain closed until about 4 a.m., when they begin to open again.	1
	(ii)	During daylight it is possible for the rate of water loss to be more than the rate of water entry.	1
		Stomata then close to protect against wilting.	1
	(iii)	Disadvantage: Transpiration will stop and the cooling effect will not take place.	1
		OR	
		Minerals will not be transported to the leaves for photosynthesis.	
		Advantage: Wilting will be prevented.	1
	(iv)	The guard cells contain chloroplasts which are used in photosynthesis during daylight to produce glucose.	1
		This is dissolved in the cell sap making a concentrated solution of sugar.	1
		The surrounding cells have a more dilute solution as cell sap, so water passes into the guard cells by osmosis.	1
		The cells swell away from the pore of the stomata and so the pore opens.	1
		During darkness, no photosynthesis takes place so no glucose can be made to form a concentrated solution and the pores close.	1

Examiner's tip This is an example of how one question can test a topic in a great deal of depth. It is unusual to have such a long question carrying so many marks, but such questions can occur on Higher tier papers. It serves to illustrate the fact that in order to opt to attempt the Higher tier, you really have to know and understand topics in detail. You are advised to obtain a copy of the syllabus that you are following to check the detail necessary for the examination. There is emphasis on both the transporting and support role of water in a plant in part (a). In part (b)(i) note that you are asked to describe what happens to the stomatal openings as seen from the graph. You are not asked to explain 'how' they open. In part (iv) you have a chance to demonstrate your knowledge of osmosis and apply it to stomatal action.

7 MOCK EXAMINATION PAPER

Question		Answer	Mark
1 (a)	(i)	37°C	1

Examiner's tip Do not forget the units °C. You might not gain credit for an answer without the units.

| | (ii) | 40.5°C | 1 |
| (b) | (i) | 10 | 1 |

Question		Answer	Mark
	(ii)	The bacteria are multiplying or dividing.	1
(c)	(i)	The bacteria are making poisonous wastes called toxins.	1
	(ii)	headache, loss of appetite, sickness. 2 x 1	2
(d)	(i)	Infectious means that the bacteria or disease can be passed on to another person.	1
	(ii)	In the air, bacteria can enter our body in the air we breath. By touching, bacteria can be passed on when you touch an infected person. In food and water, our food and drink could contain bacteria. By animals, many animal pests, like flies, settle on animal dung then walk over our skin or our food.	4
(e)		Bacteria: A, C, E	2
		Viruses: B, D	2

2

food type	food sources	use in body
carbohydrates	sugar, cakes, bread	provide energy
protein	meat/fish/chicken OR peas/beans/lentils	growth & repair
fats	butter, margarine, cooking oil	Insulate the body and as a store of energy
vitamins &/or minerals	fresh fruit and vegetables	essential for good health

One mark for each correct answer   **6**

3 (a) (i) green water plants → insect larvae → fish → otter   **1**

(ii)

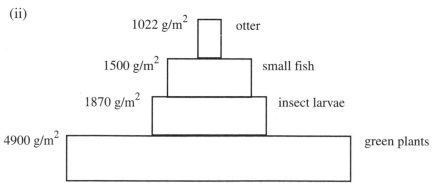

1022 g/m² — otter
1500 g/m² — small fish
1870 g/m² — insect larvae
4900 g/m² — green plants

One mark for correct proportion of size in pyramid.
One mark for labelling organisms.
One mark for biomass with units.   **3**

Question	Answer	Mark

(iii) More growth of green plants, small fish would have less to eat/some small fish might die due to lack of food, otter would have less to eat.
(any 2 points, 1 mark each) **2**

(b) Fertiliser is soluble and can be washed away in rain, resulting in eutrophication. The increase in fertiliser caused the green plants including algae to grow faster. This stops the sunlight reaching the plants at the bottom of the lake. Algae and plants at bottom of lake die and decompose, removing oxygen from the water. The lack of oxygen kills the fish.
(any 4 points, 1 mark each) **4**

4 (a) (i) B upper epidermis **1**
A cuticle **1**
C palisade layer **1**
D spongy layer **1**

(ii) Xylem tubes – carry water and salts to the leaf, **1**
Phloem tubes — take away dissolved food. **1**

(iii) Allows the diffusion of gases into and out of the leaf, allows water vapour to diffuse out. **2**

(iv) To allow the gases to diffuse through the leaf. **1**

(v) Leaves are flat,
spaced well apart to catch most sun,
leaves are able to twist to face the sun,
with a large surface area,
most chloroplasts in the palisade (top) layer so they can catch more sun,
clear cuticle to allow sun's rays to pass through,
(any 4, 1 mark for each point) **4**

(vi) $6CO_2 + 6H_2O \qquad\qquad 6O_2$
(1 mark for correct symbols, 1 mark for balanced equation) **2**

Question	Answer	Mark

(b) (i) The greater the light intensity,
the faster the rate of photosynthesis.

2

Examiner's tip This would be the accepted answer. If more marks were available a more detailed answer would be required, so you would go on to explain that: after 140W the rate of photosynthesis remains constant. This is due to limiting factors.

(ii) All coordinates correct = 2 marks
8 – 6 correct = 1 mark, less than 6 = no marks.

2

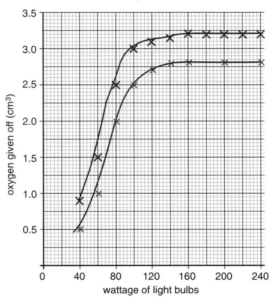

(iii) A smooth curve through most of the points.

1

Examiner's tip This is not a dot-to dot diagram, the line does not need to pass through all of the points. The line is meant to show the pattern or trend.

---

5 (a) A = sweat gland, B = blood vessel, C = hair, D = hair muscle

4

(b) (i) Sweat gland is inactive,
blood vessel becomes narrow (vasoconstriction) so less blood flows near the surface of the skin,
so less heat lost by radiation,
hair muscle forces hair to upright position,
goose bumps form,
this traps a layer of air close to the surface of the skin which insulates the body keeping heat in.

(any 4, 1 mark each)

4

(ii) For sweat to evaporate heat is required, this heat is removed from our bodies thus cooling us.

1

Examiner's tip A common misconception is that the production of sweat has a cooling effect, it is actually the evaporation of the sweat from the surface of our skin that causes the cooling effect.